THE CHICKEN MAN

Published in 1989 by
Williams-Wallace Publishers Inc.
P.O. Box 756
Stratford, Ontario, Canada
N5A 4A0

Canadian Cataloguing in Publication Data

Frolick, Gloria Kupchenko
  The Chicken Man

ISBN 0-88795-080-9 (bound) ISBN 0-88795-079-5 (pbk.)

I. Title

PS8561.R64C48 1989   C813' .54   C89-094926-3
PZ7.F77Ch 1989

Cover painting and art-work by William Kurelek.
Permission to use art work courtesy of The Issacs Gallery.

Photographs of the cover illustration and of author by
Everett Roseborough.

Photographs of black and white illustrations by Thomas Moore.

Published with the generous assistance of the Canada Council and
the Ontario Arts Council and The Multiculturalism Program,
department of the Secretary of State.

Printed and bound in Canada.

THE CHICKEN MAN

by

GLORIA KUPCHENKO-FROLICK

Williams-Wallace Publishers
Stratford, Ontario

ACKNOWLEDGEMENTS

It was in 1976 that William Kurelek wrote to me from Saskatchewan saying that he had completed the illustrations for my novel, The Chicken Man. "The cover is a surrealistic public eye-catcher," he wrote. Adding modestly, "I didn't know that I had it in me." Later he phoned to tell me how "moved" he was by John Babich's story. William Kurelek died in 1977.

I would like to acknowledge and express my sincere thanks to Everett Roseborough, a cherished friend, for photographing the cover illustration and for my photograph on the back cover.

I'd like to thank my children Deborah, Christine, Larry and Vernon for their encouragement during the writing of The Chicken Man.

A special thank you to Dr. Patricia Morley, Marvi Ricker, Gay Allison, Avrom Isaacs, Elizabeth Legge, Olha Kolankiwsky, Jean Kurelek, Lydia Palij, Christine Stodilka, Thomas Moore and Sonja Dunn for their invaluable advice and support.

To the memory of my parents Anne Perich Kupchenko and Dr. Volodymyr Kupchenko.

ILLUSTRATIONS

Errata Note:

Page 53, the correct reading of this caption should be 'Banging Barn Door.'

"The harvest is past, the summer is ended, and we are not saved."

Jeremiah: The Book of the Prophet

He had never, in all his seventy-four years, seen such opulence. Such magnificence. Never! The ornamentation of the room stunned him. Every single item in the room shimmered, sparkled. The walls of the room gleamed like polished topaz. Shielding his eyes from the brightness, John Onufrey Babich delighted over the wondrous things that filled the great hall: chests, ivories, paintings, tapestries, majestic statues. Everywhere the sparkle of crystal and gold. It was a miracle! How on earth had he stumbled upon such a place? He'd have to tell Elizabeth about this. She would really appreciate all this beauty. Elizabeth would have to come with him next time he came here. She would explain everything to him. It was all so beautiful, but so perplexing to him. How had he missed this place all these years?

Fine statues, set in alcoves along the walls, gravely regarded one another in an atmosphere of mystery, of contemplation. They appeared so life-like to Babich, he couldn't be sure they weren't confiding secrets to each other.

Gingerly crossing the marble floor as though stepping on a freshly scrubbed floor and expecting to be yelled at, Babich walked up to one of the statues — that of a serene and beautiful young woman. Bowing to her in greeting, Babich crossed himself reverently. Never had he seen such perfection, such workmanship. The young woman looked so real he could have sworn that she was smiling at him. Yes, he was sure of it. His spirits began to soar. This was a most heavenly place.

He couldn't, as hard as he tried, figure out how in the devil he'd gotten here to this palace. Obviously it *was* a palace. Had he been invited? It didn't seem likely, since there was no one to welcome him. He had the room all to himself. In fact it was so damnably silent in the room it reminded him of the winter day he'd dropped into his old schoolhouse, abandoned for some twenty years — yes, it was that eerily quiet here. Babich could feel goosebumps over his arms and legs. It wasn't that he was nervous, it was the cold. It was cold in the place; the truth was he was freezing his ass off!

Shuddering like a horse in a winter gale, Babich looked around, undecided about what he should do. It really was a bugger — the cold in the room. Imagine the owner not having the sense to keep it warm. If he could find the stove, he'd stoke up the fire himself. If he could find where they kept the wood. He could certainly do that, except that there was no way he could find the woodbox in all this jumble of goods. He couldn't figure it out. How could the owners of this grand palace be so stupid — to have such wealth, and to freeze. Strange, he thought, but people were strange.

Well, what the hell. The cold wouldn't kill him. He'd spend a few more minutes and then go home and warm up. Elizabeth would certainly find all this very interesting. Crossing himself reverently, Babich stood transfixed. Whoever would have guessed that he, John Onufrey Babich, would be this lucky. Who would have guessed it; this was really a palace; a veritable palace. Some day, when it was warmer, he'd come back and spend time here with Elizabeth.

If only it were just a whit warmer — so he could walk around without shivering. He badly needed to take a leak, but where would the outhouse be in such a place? He'd better hold it in until he got home. The cold made him want to go. His kidneys were like sieves; he couldn't hold his water worth a damn. Pissing every hour on the hour like an old baba.

He sure as hell would like to meet the fellow who built this place. Whoever built it must have been a master carpenter. Boy oh boy, you really had to give him credit. The man did a fine job! Couldn't have been anyone he knew. Now Metro Chaba, he was a pretty good carpenter, but not this good — not by a long shot! This carpenter was a genius. You really had to hand it to him. That ceiling, my God, that took some doing. Jesus! What a fine job!

Babich scratched his grizzled head and stared up at the cross-ribbed vault until his neck got a crick in it.

Dammit! Old age was no joy.

Sequins of light from hundreds of flickering candles set in a tall bronze candelabrum and in a double row of crystal chandeliers, bathed the hall in gold, the colour of buckwheat honey.

Babich stood under one of the massive, multi-tiered crystal chandeliers. He gazed up at them in open-mouthed admiration. Suddenly the massive chandelier started to sway. Gently at first, and then all the chandeliers started moving in unison until the great hall reverberated with the ringing of their crystals. He was afraid that the swaying would pull the roof down on his head. In spite of his anxiety, Babich couldn't help smiling at what sounded like the ringing of thousands of sleigh bells on a frosty night. It was beautiful — their chiming so beautiful. Still and all, why would they swing in such a strange way?

There had to be a rational explanation for the swinging. It was all so peculiar. There was no wind, and there was no one in the room. He couldn't figure it out. It was puzzling.

But now it didn't matter since the chandeliers were perfectly still with just a faint tinkling. Maybe he had just imagined it.

The real question was, how in the devil had he gotten to this place? He couldn't recall walking here. It was so peaceful here —why hadn't he come here before? Maybe he'd gotten a lift from a neighbour. But which neighbour? His head was useless — his brain, after all these years was a dried walnut in its shell.

"Ha ha ha".

The idea of his brain being no bigger than a walnut struck him as funny. He laughed out loud.

His laughter echoed throughout the great hall. It was unseemly to laugh in such a dignified place; he'd better control himself. This was like a holiday, so he might just as well enjoy himself. An opportunity like this came but once in a lifetime. To think that he, John Babich, should be so privileged! He was truly blessed to be here. It was like heaven.

Scratching vigorously at his crotch, Babich looked around furtively to make sure he hadn't been seen. His wretched long johns had shrunk so much they were cutting into him. He was chafed and it was driving him crazy. For two cents he'd take his underwear off and to hell with it! But he was freezing already, so he'd better stick it out.

As he walked along a fairly wide passage Babich nodded a greeting to all the statues. They seemed to smile directly at him; their smiles so gentle, so loving, so forgiving he could feel his spirits begin to soar. This was all quite wonderful.

Maybe he would stay awhile longer. Suddenly he felt as light as air, even the room seemed somewhat warmer — he could hear a pleasant hum in the room; reassuring like a teakettle set back on a warm stove. And he had the entire room to himself.

Clapping his hands in childlike delight. Babich walked along, chuckling in appreciation over each new discovery.

"My . . . my . . . my". Such stained glass windows; they were masterpieces. Babich stopped in his tracks. His hoarse voice echoed loudly through the room. What in the devil? His echo seemed unnaturally loud.

"My . . . my . . . my" he repeated. "My . . . my . . . my" the echo was louder than his voice. What in the devil was going on? He began to feel nervous, and a little foolish. Babich called out once again. Again the same loud echo. His voice, yet not his voice. Listening intently, Babich felt the hair rise on the back of his neck.

What was going on? *That* was no echo. Someone in the room was mocking him. Who could it be? Mimicking him so perfectly? The voice was his, but younger, more confident. There was something else in that echo — a tinge of cruelty, of malice in that voice.

Son-of-a-bitch. Who could it be? Who would taunt him this way? And why? His anxiety rose, and Babich listened for movement. There were countless places for the joker to hide. It seemed to Babich that even the statues had cocked their heads to listen with him. But there was nothing. No sound anywhere except for the hammering of his heart. Perhaps he'd better get a move on. Elizabeth would be home from school waiting for him and there were plenty of chores to be done.

It occurred to him he'd be wise to stick close to the wall on the opposite side of the room. With the shadows he'd be less conspicuous. As he crossed the marble floor Babich had an awful sense that there was a presence in the room. Tension like a clenched fist started in his belly and moved up to his chest. Dammit to hell, he was becoming afraid; really afraid.

As he reached the shadowed arcade, Babich breathed a sigh of relief. This was better, much better. He couldn't be seen in this passageway. He could take his time now. If only the terrible pain in his chest would let go of him. He had to rest. Leaning his back up against a marble column, Babich admired the fancy cross-ribbed vault.

Dizzy, Babich leaned heavily against one of the pillars, crossed his arms protectively over his chest, and closed his eyes. With his head on his chest he waited for the frightening dizziness to go away. Dammit. It was a nuisance!

Babich awoke to find himself face down on the cold floor. Had he fainted? Dozed off? Jesus! Picking himself off the floor, Babich leaned back against the pillar to steady himself.

The strangest thing! The pillar, the great massive column was moving behind him. How could it be? He gave the pillar a shove. Babich was shocked to see it rocking, as lightly as though it were made of . . . Jesus! The pillar was . . . it was paper; it was fake. It was crazy! The whole damned place was crazy. Maybe it was all fake. Well, it didn't matter. Nothing mattered. The pain in his chest was unbearable. He had to fight off a longing to lie down on the cold floor and sleep.

He'd be better off at home. So he'd better get a move on.

"Jesus . . . Holy Mother of God!" What the hell?

Recoiling in horror, Babich almost fell into a dark, slime-covered pool. What the hell was going on? The entire room was filled with stinking water. Water afloat with gouts of earth. Stinking water that made him want to retch. Water covered with connecting islands of greyish-green slime. He had nearly fallen into it. The room suddenly became so dark he could scarcely see where he stood. He could feel the slimy ledge under his bare feet. My God! Everything had gone haywire.

Babich pressed himself against the icy wall. He could make out dark forms undulating at the bottom of the pool. Hideous creatures like giant tadpoles, darted and leapt from island to island, landing with soft thuds on the slime. It was horrible . . . horrible.

What was happening? If only Elizabeth had come all this wouldn't have happened. It never would have happened.

He should never have come here, never! He inched his way along the narrow ledge, trying to find a way out. Babich realized that he'd better just squeeze against the wall and pray. This was some kind of . . . Babich couldn't bring himself to think it. He was in trouble. Deep trouble. He was being punished. He had been found out. His guilt had been exposed. Oh God . . . he was finished. This was Hell. God! Help! God! Had he ended up in Hell? Babich braced himself against the wall. He could feel the water rising. It was now lapping at his ankles. Oh, God! Not daring to look down, Babich swayed on the ledge. Sweat trickled down his trembling body. He was exhausted.

"Drip . . . drip . . . drip." His own sweat was dripping into that filthy pool. The filthy waters were rising. It was a hellish nightmare . . . that's what it was . . . a nightmare! "Help, God help me!" "Help me."

His voice, yet not his voice, cracked with fear and echoed in the eerie darkness. And that mocking voice . . . imitated him perfectly and called out piteously.

Tears welled up in his eyes. Dammit! He did not deserve this. This was terrible treatment. He had to get out. He had to! He had to find a way out of this predicament. He was losing his reason. Was he going mad?

Have mercy on me. Mercy . . . I beg of you. Elizabeth . . . My beloved Elizabeth . . . I am finished.

Then, as suddenly as the room had darkened, it was lighter again. Now he could see. Praise be to God, Now he could see how much room there was on that ledge.

Holy Mother of Jesus! A woman crossed the room, oblivious to the obvious dangers of the filthy pool. She was definitely coming in his direction. Perhaps if he looked away she wouldn't see him.

Jesus! She smiled — smiled at him. What the hell was she doing? Had she no shame? She was naked. Not a stitch on her voluptuous body. Unbelievable! She was coming straight toward him. What did she want from him? Jesus!

"Whore! Get away . . . get away from me." Waving desperately, Babich tried to shoo her away. He crossed himself, hoping to make her disappear. He mustn't . . . he mustn't look at her. She was shameless, an obscene creature. Maybe he'd only imagined her. Babich saw her skimming across the pool toward him like a dirigible. On her narrow, almost childlike head he could see a red wig —bramble-like. There was something about her. Was she someone he knew? There was no question about it — she *was* real, she *was* touching him. Her soft arms gathered him into her plump breasts. Oh Jesus! No! No! Get away . . . get away from me, you bitch! Ignoring his insults, she cocked her head coquettishly. Her red painted smile was so wide Babich could see into her throat.

"John, now don't be shy . . . you *know* you want me . . . come . . . come to me . . . I have something special for you." She gave a soft little laugh. Oh God! Her voice. It was beautiful, surprisingly gentle and feminine. And . . . she knew his name. She had called his name.

"John," she repeated, "Come, come to me."

He was trembling so much, he was afraid he'd fall off the ledge. His face and body on fire, Babich felt himself responding to her invitation. He mustn't . . . he must not. She was nothing but a scarlet woman . . . a whore . . . oh God!

Her red mouth was on his mouth, moist. He could feel his belly on fire. No! No! This is wrong . . . all wrong! He wanted her . . . her child's eyes, soft, gentle and so forgiving. God help him. He wanted, he desired — he yearned for her! Help me, someone help me. Please.

He was suffocating. Her thick lips, firm, encircled his. She was sucking out his breath . . . his life!

Oh Jesus . . . he was dying. Her nipples pressed into his chest. She flattened herself against him. "Help . . . help!" They were, both of them, sinking down into the stinking waters. He swallowed horrible things, whole. They were both drowning . . . going under.

Let go . . . let me go. With all his strength Babich pushed against her.

"Whore! Let go! Whore! Then — just like that — she disappeared. His hands held nothing. It was as if she had dissolved in his arms. There was nothing left. Only the pain in his chest. And the aching in his groin.

She seemed . . . so kind. Still she was immoral. Thank God he was saved. He hadn't committed a sin. The room was as before, bright and luminous. His eyes filled with tears. Poor creature, he almost wished she'd come back. Just to talk to him. He couldn't tell Elizabeth about the woman . . . he would have to keep it a secret. He wasn't to blame.

If only he could be certain that no one was in the room now, he'd strip, right there and then. His body was on fire. His temples were pounding. If he had the nerve, he'd strip right there and then and walk around as naked as the day he was born.

The room, back to its former glory, seemed different somehow. It was as though he were viewing the room through a kaleidoscope. Everything, colours, shapes, kept dissolving and changed minute by minute.

Yes, and to hell with anyone who'd think ill of him, he'd walk around naked.

The notion of walking around completely naked in that beautiful room excited him. His body was consumed with strange stirrings, yearnings.

He tried to walk faster but his legs refused to cooperate. Babich looked around with increasing anxiety for a way out. It was strange. There seemed to be no exit. How had he come in anyway?

A bubble of laughter threatened to explode into hysterical laughter. His lips were parched. The door. Where was the door?

There was a strange hush in the room like the eerie silence before a summer storm. He could feel a scream coming up into his throat. There was someone in the room. He could feel it. He could sense it. A terrifying presence that started to control his every movement was in the room. Oh God.

"Sh . . . whoosh. Sh . . . whoosh . . ." Babich froze. A strange whispering, a slapping sound like wet sheets flapping in a fierce wind came from the vault.

There it was again. He couldn't quite place the sound. Probably pigeons in the loft. Of course. Only pigeons in the loft . . . that's all . . . just pigeons.

He tried to sing; to give himself courage. He made several starts; but he couldn't remember the words of a single song. His mind went blank.

Humming tunelessly, he continued, urgently, to look for a way out. There was a buzzing in his head. Rational thinking had evaporated; his mind see-sawed.

He could feel it. Something terrible was going to happen. Something in the room was finally going to get him. Oh please — don't abandon me. Not here in this hell. Someone . . .

The air around him turned icy cold, as if someone had opened a door in to winter. He knew it then. He knew that the thing he feared most was in this room.

He could smell it even before he saw it. An ugly bird, a black, hideous bird with ungainly wings was diving right at him. And there it was, that noise — Sh . . . whoosh. Sh . . . whoosh. The bird was right on top of him. The bird's steel grey talons, before his eyes now, stinking with carrion. Those filthy claws tore into his arms, his chest.

Black Bird

Babich could feel his mouth forming cries, but no sounds came forth. Swallowing scream after scream, Babich fell to the floor.

Curling into a fetal position, he rolled away from the hideous claws. But the bird swooped down at him. Pitiless, malevolent, human eyes that looked into his eyes. He could see revenge, triumph, victory in those remorseless eyes.

He knew it then. The voice he heard had come from this unearthly creature; an avenging angel of death — and it had been waiting there, up in that loft, all of these years, waiting for this moment.

Babich began to pray. *Dear God in Heaven, help me, help me, a wretched sinner. Forgive a sinner.* His voice, desperate, echoed in this horrible room. *Sinner . . . sinner . . . sinner.*

Babich shut his eyes — waited for the end, for the bird to finish him off. Agonizing moments passed. He waited for the burning pain of claws. To his relief, he heard the rustle of wings. The bird was gone. Like that! The bird was gone.

Babich struggled to his feet. He must get out of here before the bird returned. The door. Where was that door? Oh God where was the door? The bird would return. He was sure of it. He had to hurry. There wasn't much time. Oh God. Keep me. Help me find that door.

However, his weary body refused to respond to this desperate need to get out. The joints in his knees locked. He dragged one foot, then the other but he wasn't making any progress at all.

Why hadn't he realized it? There — blocking his path — was an exquisitely carved altar which soared right up into a dark vault. Yes, of course, of course, he was in a church . . . a cathedral. For shame, for shame, not to have realized it from the beginning.

Painfully, Babich knelt before the altar. Sobbing with gratitude and relief, Babich started to pray. Rocking on his knees, Babich called up to heaven. *"Forgive me . . . forgive me."* He repeated these words endlessly, remaining on his knees. His teeth chattered. He was cold, utterly exhausted. His face was streaked with tears:

"Forgive me . . . forgive me."

And there it was again — that terrible creature — that hellish bird mocking him. But they couldn't trick him. He knew exactly what was going on. He wasn't going to fight anymore.

Babich chuckled. "You out there! Yes . . . you . . . hiding there." Babich pointed a trembling finger up to the loft. "You there! I'm on to you. You can't fool me! You think you're so smart! Making fun of an old man! Old Babich isn't that stupid. I know what's going on! I'm on to you. I'm dreaming. All of this." Babich threw his arms out wide to encompass the entire room — the whole world — "All of this is nothing but a dream. A bad dream. A nightmare! You don't scare me one bit! Hey! You . . . you . . . out there! Babich clenched his fist, shaking it at the unseen presence in the loft. Come out of there. Come out and show yourself. I'm not afraid of you. Come and show yourself — like a man!"

His bravado increased with his insults. "You . . . you dog-shit . . . you . . . you asshole." He was thoroughly enjoying himself now. He felt fearless. Strong. Invincible. Never would he be afraid again. "Do you hear me up there?" He shouted now. He didn't care what he said. Once and for all, whoever it was up there, he was going to tell him off, he was going to say exactly what he thought of his tormentor.

"Come here, you . . . you son-of-a-bitch . . . you . . . hypocrite . . . you . . . you . . . you son-of-a-whore!"

What had he just said? What if . . . what if . . . he weren't dreaming? What if all of this *was* real. Oh my God. He'd get it for sure. He'd be in trouble. A peck of trouble!

He'd better get the hell out of here while the getting was good. Where was the door? Where in the devil was the door?

Babich started to run, frantically, searching for a way out. The door, the door . . . no, not there . . . where . . . not here. Oh God the door, please. Where, oh where was the door?

Then it hit him like a hammer. A blow to his temple! There was no door! He'd never get out! The bird would be back. It was only resting. In that shadowed vault, waiting to get back at him, to finish him off. The bird would return. This was no dream.

Strangely, calmed by this sobering realization, Babich crossed himself. Calmly, this time, with deliberate movements. With a serenity that surprised and pleased him. He crossed himself three times. Tears filled his eyes, washed down his cheeks. Smiling through his tears Babich yelled out teasingly. "Hey you, you up there, I know, I know there's no way out."

But in spite of this certain knowledge, Babich pushed stubbornly. He pushed with all his might, pushed at the solid, unmovable wall. The wall started to give way . . . he was . . . he was breaking down the wall . . . he was . . . he was *free!* He could hear birds chirping. He was right not to give up. He was free . . . free! Home free! Praise be to God.

He looked around in a daze, and rubbed his sleepcrusted eyes. Babich looked around in delight. He was safe. Perfectly safe. He was awake and alive — in his own bed, in his own room. Praise be to God! It was a bad dream. He, John Onufrey Babich, was awake, alive, and safe, in his very own bed, his own bedroom, his own house. Praise be to God! He was alive and well. Alive and well. Praise be to God!

He heard the chirping of birds, hovered between sleep and consciousness as the chirping grew louder. He opened his eyes, slowly. Thank God! He was safe in his own bed. Safe in his own bedroom. He'd had that terrible nightmare again. But every time he closed his eyes the terrible images of sleep returned. He forced himself to sit up. He concentrated on the birds outside. He began organizing in his mind the work that needed doing that day.

Mrs. Ellefson would be coming tomorrow, she said she'd take all the tomatoes he could spare. But that terrible dream — what did it mean? His head was swimming. He had to get up. Get out of bed. John Babich, get a move on. Another day of work waiting. God, he felt so dizzy.

He leaned back for a moment, rested his head against the cool metal of the headboard. The bedding was a tangled mess, and he was soaked, drenched with sweat. He was bathed in sweat — his long underwear, his pillows, his sheets, were soaking wet. He couldn't seem to catch his breath in this stinking room, smelling of his own sweat. Babich licked his parched lips, tried to swallow, but his mouth was dry as dust. He needed air, fresh air. He grabbed the rungs of the headboard, managed to heave himself into a sitting position. Now he felt better — a bit shaky — but much better.

It was easier breathing sitting up. Son-of-a-bitch. The goddam bedroom smelled like an outhouse! Babich sat on the edge of the bed, waited for the hammering of his heart to slow down. No wonder he was suffocating. The bedroom needed airing.

The memory of last night's dream returned for a second. It haunted him and tears welled up in his eyes. Was he to have no peace — even in his sleep? Was he to be plagued by those cursed dreams all his life? Would he never be free?

Thank God dawn was breaking. Each morning he seemed to be getting up earlier. It was hell lying in bed staring into darkness, feeling he was the only person alive on earth. Well, there was a lot of work to do in the garden, a lot of work to do so today.

Damned if his head wasn't spinning. His head lowered between his knees, he sat bent over for a moment until his head cleared, then he got up and crossed the bedroom floor to the open window. It was cold in the unheated bedroom. He shivered as he reached for his shoes under the bed. He retrieved one and used it as a hammer. He hit the window frame several times, managed to raise it higher to let in more air. He needed it.

Babich took several breaths of fresh, cold, morning air. He swung his arms in a circle, up and around, in an effort to get his circulation going.

A small pile of leaves that had been trapped on the window sill lifted as a sudden gust of wind blew into the bedroom. Dust and lint balls floated from under the bed, joined the dry leaves and settled in a heap under the dresser. There was no getting away from it. The house needed a good cleaning from top to bottom. Babich groaned and bent to pick his workclothes up from the heap on the floor. It was too cold to dress in the bedroom. He carried his overalls and sweater into the kitchen and stood beside the still warm stove. He would dress for another day of work in his beloved garden.

By the looks of it, he was going to have a beautiful day. Even the burrs that he found matting the back of his sweater failed to dampen the pleasure he felt at the prospect of gathering vegetables from his garden. This year the garden was beautiful. He could be forgiven for boasting for no one in the district had such fine tomatoes. Why they were perfect — firm, unblemished and absolutely delicious. He'd staked all the tomato plants extra carefully this year. But he'd have to watch the neighbour's children again. The little buggers from across the way liked to sneak into his garden and steal his vegetables.

Why only last fall he'd gone into town for a few hours when he had come home to find the garden almost demolished, and most of the tomatoes gone. The ones they didn't take they smashed against the house and barn. Tomatoes lay everywhere, squashed. It had broken his heart to see such waste. Well, this year he'd fool them. He wouldn't leave the house, even for one minute, until he'd picked the garden clean . . . damned if he would! Little buggers. Good-for-nothing woman to let her children run around like wild animals.

Babich pulled the last burr off his sweater. He watched as it burned and sizzled on the embers of last night's fire. He pulled his sweater over his head, not bothering to unbutton it. He stepped into his mud-caked overalls and tried several times before he was able to close the safety pin that held his sweater closed at the neck — where the top button was missing.

If only the little buggers had asked him, he'd have given them all the tomatoes they wanted, but no, they preferred to sneak around when he was away. That mother of theirs, parading around in that wig and those short skirts, exposing her cooked-ham thighs. It's no wonder she had no time to cook them a decent meal.

Swearing with exasperation, Babich found two large blue-bottle flies floating in the last of his butter. Stupid head, he'd left the butter dish on the window sill, instead of covering it, hiding it in the cool pantry. Now there would be no butter for his breakfast. Served him right! What's an old man to do with such a head?

Babich took several small pieces of wood from the oven, where he'd been drying it overnight. When the wood caught fire, he added several larger pieces to the stove. When the fire was burning well, he stoked up the stove and replaced the stove lid. Thank God for some things that worked. Dry wood that burned well was a blessing.

Here he was, uncomfortable as the devil, his belly near bursting from his need to take a leak and him standing here, all this time, suffering. Babich stepped outside in his bare feet, and looked carefully up and down the road, satisfying himself that there was no one around to see him. He relieved himself into weeds growing against the house. Now he felt better, much better.

Thank God his socks had dried overnight. There was nothing more miserable than wearing wet, woollen socks. Babich pulled up a kitchen chair near the stove, and sat down to pull on his socks. The kitchen looked neat as a pin. He looked around with satisfaction. He'd done a pretty good job last night — everything was tidy in its place and the floor was swept up.

He hadn't noticed the smear on the floor last night near the stove where he'd spilled the ashes. It seemed clean enough last night. Wouldn't harm though to give the floor a good scrubbing with soap and water. He'd do it tonight, after supper, if only that pain didn't return — to plague him. Babich removed several pieces of still damp wood from the woodbox and piled them into the oven to dry, aligning the pieces to his satisfaction. There was nothing like tamarack when it was good and dry.

That pain last night — probably it was nothing more than indigestion. That'd teach him to stay away from fried pork. Babich pulled his chair closer to the stove, warmed himself. Much as he hated admitting it, he was tired. Hardly out of bed, and damned if he wasn't tired!

Babich rested his feet on the open oven door and looked around the room. The morning sun cast a pattern of light on the walls and ceiling. Babich followed the dancing spots as they flitted about the room.

He felt so strange this morning. As though he'd just recovered from a long illness. Everything in the room stood out. Everything appeared clear and distinct. So well-defined, it was as though he were seeing the room and all of the things in it for the first time. He looked around the room where he'd spent all his life with bright new interest.

The next time he went into town he'd get a new oil cloth for the table. He could certainly afford a new tablecloth. This one was shamefully worn out; he couldn't even remember when he'd bought it. All that remained of the pattern was a hint of blue checks around the edge. The corners were torn and hanging and the wooden table showed through. Yes, it was certainly time he got some things for the house. He'd buy a bright, cheerful cloth — spruce up the house for Christmas, maybe even invite some of the neighbours over.

He needed some fresh water for making breakfast. Both water pails were nearly empty, but he continued to sit there, with his feet on the oven door, warming his hands over the stove.

He should have gotten rid of that foolish thing years ago. Goes to show how foolish an old man can get. A sunbeam danced about, flickering over the face of a doll, seated on the old trunk by the door. It was unnatural, that doll — almost as big as a child. How Elizabeth had laughed over it — like a little girl herself. A Christmas card had come with it and he kept coming across it all the time, somewhere there in a shoe box in the dresser. Every time he'd come upon it, he'd read the message of love written inside, in that careful childish hand — the signatures of all her little pupils — thirty-four names, thirty-four little children all grown up long ago. All probably with grown children of their own. Scattered around the four corners of this earth, all having forgotten about their teacher, his dear Elizabeth.

How pleased she'd been with that toy — that silly doll — held it to her and danced around the room laughing with delight. Well, that silly toy was nothing but a dust collector, like everything else in the house. He felt like crying but no, he wasn't going to cry, there was no point in useless tears. He'd shed enough. The doll's glassy blue eyes cast a curious glance. Damned if the stupid thing didn't give him the shivers — made him feel uneasy. It was sacrilegious to make toys like so life-like. He should have given it to some child long ago. Well, there was work to do and water to bring in and he couldn't sit around all morning thinking such nonsense.

Babich added several pieces of wood to the fire, picked up the two water pails, emptied the rest of the water left in one of them into a wash basin and placed the basin on the back of the stove. His rubber boots were outside on the stoop where he'd left them last night. He tried to step into them, but lost his balance, almost fell. He was furious with himself. He put down the two pails, sat on one

The Pail

of the upper steps and pulled on his mud-covered boots. It was so discouraging. He was tired already. Everything he did tired him out these days. Sometimes it seemed that life was hopeless.

Babich closed his eyes and turned his face to the warmth of the morning sun. It was so pleasant sitting here, the sun on his face, he could sit here like this all day. Sit here, not moving until the end came. Until, one day, the neighbour's children would find him — a withered old scarecrow, still holding on to the two pails in his hands. Or maybe some hungry dog would find him and drag him away — bury him somewhere like an old bone! He laughed out loud at the thought. He looked around quickly. It wouldn't do for people to hear him laughing out loud like this. They'd think forsure old man Babich was a lunatic. Ready for Ponoka.

No, he wouldn't give in. Never. Even if it killed him. He would *not* give in to old age. There was a lot of work to do today. It was no good sitting here, feeling sorry for himself. But still, there was no getting away from it. He was getting old and clumsy. He'd better be more careful. Just yesterday, he'd slipped on the wet grass near the pump. His bottom lip was still sore and swollen. And last night when he lay down, he had to be careful to lie on his right side because the cut on his head where he'd hit himself on the cement casing hurt so much he couldn't fall asleep.

What's a person to do? What can one do, when you are old and getting careless, and the old head refuses to work properly? Babich filled one pail, put it down on the sidewalk and stopped to rest, to look over his garden. No one could deny it. Everything in the garden was beautiful. Everything looked fresh and beautiful in the soft light of morning. No one could say that this wasn't a perfect garden! All the vegetables were growing in neat rows and all the rows as straight as arrows. A tall goldenrod near the cucumbers caught his eye. How had he missed such an ugly weed? He walked carefully between the rows, pulled it out, and threw it over the fence into the pasture.

Next year, maybe, he'd experiment a bit. Those Russian cucumbers in the seed catalogue looked good. Maybe plant a hill or two, just to try them out. No harm in trying. Babich was breathing heavily by the time he'd half-filled the second pail so he had to take time out to rest again. Every year he'd planted sunflowers along the fence. They formed a stately row along the entire length of the garden. He couldn't recall them ever being this tall and healthy, their heads so large and well-formed. Queen Anne's lace, golden-rod, Scotch thistles, purple vetch, yarrow and burdock also grew thickly along the fence that divided the yard from the pasture. How displeased his father would be at the sight of those weeds.

He could hear his father's voice, scornful, as he talked of farmers who permitted their farms to become weed-infested. To his father, a man like that was no "gazda," not even worth talking to. Once, this yard too, had been as well-kept as a park. Once, there hadn't been a single weed in this entire yard. Maybe he should have taken that smart-alec young doctor's advice. Maybe he should have sold his farm the way Chorney did. And move into the old folk's home in Vegreville. He was no good to himself, no use to anyone, for that matter. But just the thought of the old folk's home agitated him. The thought of it was unbearable. What did that young doctor know? He was managing all right. God, the people were old people he had seen in the home that day — *old people.*

He wasn't *that* old — not by a long shot! Scared the shit out of him though, seeing all those oldsters. Sitting there, warming them-selves in the sun, and farting in front of that wretched TV in a fancy parlour. No sir, that old folk's home wasn't for him. Having that good-looking, big-assed *young* woman telling him what to do, where to sit, when to eat. Old folk's home indeed! He wasn't old folks yet!

"Son-of-a-bitch." Babich cleared his throat. Spat out his

anger. Old enough to be that young woman's grandfather! Now he was angry, but his fatigue had gone. Shit no! He wasn't dead yet! Those old people, sitting there with hands folded in their laps, waiting for God to take them away! It was a sin. Against God, that's what it was, and a disgrace to give up that way! He filled the second pail so quickly that the water spilled over the top. Already he was feeling better. He was even getting hungry. Babich walked back to the house, carefully balancing the two pails of water so as not to spill more than necessary.

A large green pick-up truck rumbled along the road past his house. Babich stopped to see if it would turn into his yard, but it disappeared over the hill, and left a cloud of dust that rolled toward the house. Disappointed, Babich walked into the house. No one visited an old man. No one cared whether he lived or died. No one cared about him. He would die alone. Like some old dog. Forgotten by everyone.

There was hardly enough coffee left in the tin for one cup. Well, never mind. This would have to do. Coffee was getting to be a real luxury. Babich tapped at the tin to get out the last grain of coffee. He wasn't too fussy. As long as the coffee was good and hot. When he'd filled the enamel pot almost to the top with fresh cold water, he was feeling more cheerful. Like it or not, he'd have to go into town soon. If it weren't for the children, he could go into town with the Elefsons, but the children would be home from school tomorrow. Maybe Monday or Tuesday he could get a ride in with someone. Last time a nice, red-cheeked young woman drove him into town and waited to bring him back. Darned if she didn't take him right to the door. Kind woman. God bless her and give her health.

There was still some porridge in the double-boiler left over from breakfast yesterday. Babich examined it, debated whether to throw it out. He decided against wasting it, added some water to it and stirred until it was bubbling. When it was hot and free of lumps he sprinkled some sugar over it. He drowned the porridge in the last of the cream. It tasted delicious. Porridge never failed to comfort him. He could tackle anything now. He poured the last of the cream into his mouth.

Yesterday had been his lucky day. He had gone down into the cellar to look for some empty jars, when he made a lucky find. Two lucky finds. He'd found a case of quart sealers, brand new, the case still unopened. And when he'd removed the carton he'd found this jar hidden behind the case — so dusty that he'd almost missed it —a nice jar of blueberry jam. Just when he was wishing for a taste of something a little sweet, there it was! He'd wiped the jar off last night. Now when he held it up to the window, he was relieved to see that it still looked good. God knows how long it must have been sitting there, or who had given it to him. The coffee started to boil, so Babich moved it to the side. He pulled a loaf of bread from the large crock he kept in the pantry. He took out a paring knife from the clutter in the cupboard drawer and pried off the small white disc of wax from the jam. There was a bit of jam sticking to the wax, so he licked it off carefully, before throwing it into the slop-pail. He'd forgotten how good wild blueberry jam tasted. Why was it that the smell, and taste of wild blueberries always brought with it such a flood of memories?

By the time he'd finished his cup of coffee and eaten his bread and jam, tears ran down his cheeks. There was just no end to the tears. Would they never cease? Here he was, sitting around crying like an old woman. He let the tears flow, and continued to look out the window, lost in mournful reverie.

He'd always loved picking mushrooms and berries. Berries of all kinds, it didn't matter to him. For him, berry-picking had been a holiday, the only holiday he ever got when he was a boy — a break from constant farm chores. The year they were married he'd talked Elizabeth into going berry-picking with him. She started out quite enthusiastically, then she'd gotten bored and restless. She'd wander around the edge of the muskeg picking bouquets of wild flowers. She'd call out to him in delight whenever she found something that interested or pleased her. His Elizabeth. She'd been like a happy child. The coffee on the stove sputtered, boiled over, and Babich, unaware, stared out the window, tears falling.

He remembered that day. They had come upon the Mazurenko's with all their children. The two youngest, both Elizabeth's pupils, had taken her by the hand, anxious to show her something. Elizabeth had insisted that he come too. That's when they both discovered the little spring. All of them had taken turns drinking the icy water from a soup plate. Such a clear spring that bubbled out of the mossy ground. Those were golden days. Golden days, all so long ago now. They were only children then, Elizabeth not yet twenty, and he, just twenty-six. But everything was changed, everyone gone. Nothing left for an old man, but fading memories. Babich sat for a long time. The coffee bubbled and boiled over on the stove.

Babich was deep in thought. Why had it taken them so long? He'd been sitting in that small waiting room for so long. The hospital had seemed so quiet. Crepe-soled shoes squished down the corridor. He had wondered if they were all hurrying to Elizabeth's room. Unable to pray, he'd sat there, thinking she'd be all right. Thank God, he'd got her to the hospital. He hated hospitals. It made him sick just going into a hospital, even to visit someone. Every time he had heard footsteps, he'd looked up. He remembered getting up, looking out into the dimly-lit courtyard, seeing the large statue of Christ. He thought he should pray. Pray to God to help him, but he couldn't. He had no right to pray. The clock in the waiting room ticked away. He'd gone to the toilet, his mind blank with fear. He was returning when he saw the doctor coming toward him, from the other end of the corridor. And he had known right away. He had known before the doctor said a single word. *Elizabeth was dead.*

The doctor avoided his eyes, placed a soft hand on his wrist. He had looked at the doctor, but couldn't follow the rest of the words at all. Afterwards, and years later, he remembered that the doctor had said, "I'm sorry, John. We tried everything." He even added, "She was a lovely young woman." The days that followed became a nightmare of events.

Elizabeth was dead. His life was over. He was finished. He had asked himself the same question, over and over. Why had it happened? Why did his beautiful Elizabeth have to die? With the passing years, he had remembered that the doctor's eyes had softened when he had said that Elizabeth, *his wife,* had been a lovely young woman. The funeral over, he had burned the bedding. He hauled out the mattress and the bloodsoaked sheets, poured gasoline over everything and watched the flames in the crisp morning air. He believed he would never, ever, be happy again. He had unravelled. The doctor's words had started him unravelling. Soon there would be nothing left of him, stitch by stitch, he was being pulled apart.

For months after his Elizabeth's death, people came to visit him, relatives, friends and neighbours. Now, there was no one. His friends were all gone. Bit by bit people had forgotten him. His mother had even tried to marry him off. Poor soul, she had never given up hope. Until her dying day she had asked him if there wasn't some nice woman. But he had preferred it this way. There were some years when he didn't think he'd survive. When life was plain misery. When all he wanted was to be left alone. God knows, no one could have stood him in those days. His friend Peter had stood by him for awhile. Everything had fallen apart for him. He'd been so angry at the world.

God forgive him, he had trusted no one. Even in church it seemed that people whispered about him. He would stand at the back of the church, on the men's side, feel all the women's eyes upon him. Sure, he knew they were all whispering about him. For a long time, he'd stopped going — it had become too hard to face people.

That spring, years back, when it had snowed in June, he'd kept the baby chicks and goslings in the kitchen under the stove and he'd gone into town to buy something. It was true. He had to admit it, he had become somewhat careless about his appearance. That day in town he passed a group of young girls, standing together in front of the Red and White store. Being still young, and shy — he'd had to steel himself to pass by them, feeling their eyes boring into his back. His face had burned for a long time with the memory of it. One of the girls, about ten or so, had walked away from the giggling girls. She had run up ahead of him, and skipped backwards, looked him boldly in the eye. Her eyes, bright with daring, looked straight at him, and she recited a little verse. Maybe he had deserved it. She had been right of course, his mackinaw had been stained, and he'd stopped sprucing up. His father had warned him, maybe he would become an oddball. But it rankled him to this day, when he recalled the words the girl recited defiantly that day — he could still hear her laughter, and the burst of laughter from the other young girls: *"Chicken-man, Chicken-man, stinks and smells, When he comes near, you'd better run like hell."* The cruel words had burned into his brain. Every time he went into town he imagined someone reciting those words behind his back. He hated going out — even to church — he hated going anywhere.

To tell the truth, he had become a recluse, and on Sundays, instead of going to church, he had taken to sitting in the shelter of a grove of Jackpines near the swamp. He'd sit alone for hours listening to the frogs, watching the ducks land on the water. He would sit there dreaming, and as time went by, he had started feeling better. Nothing bothered him anymore. His heart had shrivelled up. But the black agony and the rage were gone.

There had been one couple who continued to visit him after Elizabeth's death. He was always pleased to see them; he had liked them both. The man had been the principal of the school where Elizabeth had taught. They never pried into his business. They were gentle, a courteous couple. The man had gone to teach somewhere in Southern Alberta. He'd received a couple of Christmas cards from them, but now he couldn't even remember their names.

It was the year Elizabeth had died when he was working in the garden, cleaning up. The couple had dropped in for a visit. They had stood around in the garden talking and he hadn't even invited them in, or offered them something to eat. He was ashamed about his lack of hospitality. But the house wasn't clean, and he had nothing suitable to offer them, so instead, he'd gathered some eggs for them, gave them some firewood. He had filled the back seat of their car with it. That day stood out so clearly in his mind, as though it had just happened. They were standing near their car, the three of them, when the honking of Canada Geese overhead had caught their attention. The geese were going south for the winter. They all stopped to watch as the thin grey line of geese grouped and regrouped. They had watched until the geese had faded from view. It was a dull November sky, grey with only the faint sound of honking in the air. His friends had said goodbye to him and were already in the car when the wife, her cheeks flushed, had run out of the car, back to where he stood, embraced him and ran back. He hadn't told them, but that day was his birthday — it was November 8th.

He'd gone into his empty, dreary house and unable to move his limbs. He had never felt so alone — so deserted. He had no desire to live that year. Every day after that he had started to think about suicide, how much easier it would be. God forgive him, but he had thought of suicide so often it had become his constant companion.

The Farm House

He had gone on living though, and somehow, the dark days passed, and the months, and years. God knows — all those years he'd been a miserable human being and his friend Peter, how could he have stood him. What a loyal friend he'd been. Even when he was in that black mood he found himself in. A black mood that wouldn't leave. Dear Peter, he'd even asked for me when he was dying. And I wasn't there. Grandmother Rachel had loved Peter, he'd made her and his mother laugh. All he had to do was appear on the doorstep and his mother's eyes would light up. Poor mother didn't have much to smile about in those days. She worked from dawn 'til dusk, as hard as any man. It's no wonder she cried so much.

What did I know, as a child? How often he had I wished she'd stop her crying. Once, he'd come upon his parents quarrelling in their bedroom. His father was shouting and had slammed out of the house. When he'd come into the bedroom, his mother was lying on the bed, her face in the pillow, her shoulders heaving. He felt relieved, thinking that maybe for once, she was laughing instead of crying. He had jumped up on the bed beside her, tugged at her hands, to pull them away from her face. He had started laughing when she refused to let him see her face. His laughter had puzzled her. When he saw that she'd been crying again, he had burst into tears. Like mother like son, his father had said when he had found them both sitting and crying on the bed. Grandmother Babich, however, was always cheerful and laughing. Nothing ever upset her.

His first memory of his grandmother was her plump figure bobbing, as she weeded their large garden. He couldn't remember whether she had told him about this, or whether he actually remembered it, but with his parents working in the fields all day, and with all the work she had to do around the house, his grandmother had to devise a harness to keep him safe. She told him how he'd run away the minute her eyes were off him — he'd be off like the wind — he loved hearing about how she'd find him wandering about like a little gypsy. She had to harness him with a rope around her waist, the other end attached to a ring that she'd slip on to the clothesline or fence. It depended on where she was working whether he would have some freedom of movement, at least he'd go no further than the length of rope. She lived in constant fear of his getting hurt. She would always cross herself when he did something dangerous. He remembered how he'd hated wearing something on his head. To this day, he preferred being bare-headed, even in cold weather. His grandmother would insist on tying one of her big kerchiefs on his head, and whenever he'd untie it and throw it down on the ground, she'd hurry over to him, and retie it. Then she'd always pick him up and crush him to her so hard he could scarcely breathe. She'd give him a kiss and call him her own little Ivan, her own little dumpling.

He could never remember his mother kissing him. But he knew that she'd loved him. His one clear childhood memory of her was seeing her dress to go out to work in the fields. She'd put on a pair of his father's pants that were too big for her. He hated seeing her dressed like that. When he was older, he remembered a parcel arriving from Eaton's, and how excited she was when she'd opened it. It was her Easter coat. Her hands had trembled when she buttoned the coat. For the first time he noticed his mother's hands — how coarse and black they looked as she touched the softness of her new coat. She'd never had much. As a small boy, he had dreamed about buying her beautiful clothes. The few times he'd seen her laughing were times when his friend Peter would come over, and they'd be doing their homework at the kitchen table. His mother would take time out from her chores, sit beside them, her eyes shining as she asked them questions about their work, about their teacher. Peter would sit there, cheerful, eating his grandmother's doughnuts. He'd tell her stories and everything he said made his mother laugh. Babich had also wanted to make her laugh, but it just wasn't in him. He had always been such a worrier, even as a small boy.

His father would always be so disgusted with him and his mother, saying that *her* son was "some hero". Then they'd quarrel because she'd always come to his defence. Even on the first day of school, how afraid he'd been. He'd worried for days that somehow he'd disgrace himself. His grandmother and his mother had both dressed him. But when he was almost ready to leave for school, his father had decided that he didn't need to wear his new shoes to school. He said it was warm enough to go barefooted. He'd said that money didn't grow on trees, and that it would be soon cold enough when he'd have to wear them, and wear them out, soon enough too! His mother and grandmother had protested, that surely on the first day . . . But he'd gone to school barefooted and he really hadn't minded. He'd hardly ever worn shoes, except in winter. He'd arrived at school early. There was no one in the schoolyard. It was chilly outside, so he stood against the side of the school, warming himself in the morning sun and holding on tightly to his new scribbler and box of crayons. A big boy had come up to him, a boy with a head like a large turnip, and a mouth full of crooked teeth. He had started taunting him, saying, didn't he own any shoes, was his father a "cheapskate or something"? He'd been so terrified, he had just stood there, not saying a word. "Cat got your tongue?" the turnip-head boy had asked. There he was, crying in front of all the children. Didn't he know that he should have worn shoes, the boy kept asking him. He had looked down in horror at his dusty feet and had tried to wipe them off. But he only managed to get his hands dusty. The teacher would make him go home. How would he explain to his father? His father would never understand. Children poured into the schoolyard, hundreds of them, all staring at him and all wearing shoes. Shoes of all kinds — patent shoes, felt shoes, sandals, boots — but all wearing shoes. The turnip-headed boy poked at him with a ruler, jabbed at him. But he had just stood there — when another big boy walked up to them — a big blonde boy, fat, with smiling blue eyes, and awkward, sloping shoulders. The blonde boy had told the cruel boy to leave him alone, to "beat it." He even said that he, John, was his best friend. And, miracle of miracles, the boy with the crooked teeth had beat it. This was how he'd found a new friend, Peter Chorney, who was, praise be, also barefooted. That had been his first meeting with Peter Chorney, and they had been friends until Chorney up and died on him. It was as if he had played a trick on him —abandoned him — and died last Christmas.

He had been a loyal friend, God rest his soul. His widow Sophie, lived in Edmonton now. A hardworking and ambitious German had bought their farm, a place where he'd spent a happy childhood. The house was boarded up and even now, after all these years, he found himself looking in the direction of their farm —looking for the light in the window. The Chorneys and their farm had been his one remaining link with his youth, with the past. He could still see Peter running through the Chorney wheatfields to visit him, while he waited with excitement in the willow thicket that grew along the fence that divided their farms. No one in school could match Peter's Tarzan yell. It was perfect. Peter's father had owned the first radio in the district, a beautiful Admiral; and Peter had picked up the Tarzan yell from a radio programme he had heard.

"Aaaa-eeyaa-eeyaa-eeoo!" How his heart quickened at the sound. Peter had worked on it until it was perfect. He'd squat in the cool willow thicket and answer Peter with a coyote call. They'd fall into each others arms laughing with the joy of it, the joy of living.

Now the Chorney house was boarded up, dark. A light coming from their windows cheered him up, even in the dead of winter, when the wind howled and snow blew across the fields. And when his beloved garden was under a thick blanket of snow, he'd only have to look out his kitchen window, see their light across the field and immediately he would feel better. Everything had changed now, neighbours had moved away, some had died. The community hall down the road — where he'd spent so many happy evenings, at Christmas concerts, at Shevchenko concerts, and where his mother and grandmother had helped at so many bazaars — was also boarded up. Weeds poked through the front steps. Even the little church where he'd been baptized had been dragged away. God knows where it had gone. Probably made into a museum where people paid admission. It wouldn't surprise him. All that remained of the past was the cemetery and God knows, he'd been cheating death long enough, one of these days it would snatch him up too! There was no one left — no one wanted old people. There was no country for the old, but there was plenty of room for the dead. Plenty of room. Babich smiled at his black mood. He was surely becoming an old woman.

Just this summer something had happened that had upset him for days. A thing of no great consequence, but still and all, it had upset him. He'd been weeding the garden when he'd heard a sound like muffled laughter coming from behind the barn. He had stopped weeding, looked around and listened, thinking the wind was playing tricks on him, thinking it was his imagination. It wasn't though. He'd found a number of children behind the barn and they scattered like mice when he'd walked up to them. All of them, that is, except for one little girl, who became so frightened she hadn't moved. Of course, he'd meant no harm to her, but he told her to go, to go on home with the other children. Maybe he had spoken too harshly to her because she scrambled under the fence crying as she ran. Was he such a monster, he'd wondered, that children ran from him in fear? The little girl's face, no bigger than his fist, eyes swimming in tears, haunted him for days. When she ran her skinny

Rainbow Over Chorney's Barn

legs moved, uncertain and awkwardly, like a newborn colt. Elizabeth had looked like that child. He had a picture of her, taken in Gavinchuk's Studio, in Smoky Lake, and she looked just like that. In the photograph, she was leaning toward her father. She looked cheerful, a sparrow, with her head cocked to the side, and one skinny leg bent over the other leg. There was no need to say it, it was madness to even think it. But they would have had a little girl like that. That picture of Elizabeth was somewhere in the drawer of the sideboard in the "good" room. One of these days he'd have to organize the pictures scattered in the drawers and fill up the empty album with them. Maybe one of these days when he finished with the garden. It would give him something to do when winter set in, though God knows, who'd want those pictures, or care about them when he was gone. Still, might be a good idea to see if the album was where he thought it was.

Babich hadn't used the "good" room for years. To save himself work, as well as fuel, he had sealed off the room and moved the washstand in front of the door. Now Babich moved the washstand out of the way and stood in the doorway for a moment, in the sunlight. The sun was so bright it made him dizzy. He lowered his head into his hands, rubbed his eyes with the heel of his hand. He looked around the room, a rush of feelings and forgotten memories washed over him. It was as if he had unlocked a part of himself, a part he had closed off for years. As though he had entered a tomb. The room smelled of damp earth, rotting, and of wet soot. Dust lay on the window sills, on the large round table, the heavy sideboard and the lace curtains, too, were grey with dust. A large cobweb hung from the curtain, attached itself to the sideboard. Babich picked a doily from the arm of the sofa and hit at the cobweb until it dropped. Then carefully, he replaced the doily. The Gurney space heater he'd bought the winter before Elizabeth had died. Rain had leaked through the chimney opening, and the wall behind the stove was streaked with soot. Rust and soot spotted the floor behind the stove. His mother had been so proud of this room.

Babich pulled up one of the heavy chairs from the table and sat down. There had been flowers growing here — ferns and geraniums and bleeding hearts — flowers on the windowsill, and flowers in the planter made of woven willow. His mother had bought the planter and some picture frames from a young man during the early 30s. The earth in the flower tins was as grey as ash and looked rock hard. What a fuss the wedding guests had made over that silver-plated tea service! His god-mother Anna Yurkiw had given it to them. Everyone had said it was a royal gift — they had never used it, not once, and now it was tarnished. No amount of polishing would ever restore it to its former beauty. Dear grandmother had made those roses. Years of exposure to the sun had bleached the bright red waxed petals to a greyish-white, so that they resembled funeral wreaths exposed to the sun and snow. Babich sat on the stiff-backed chair, taking inventory of the silent room. His dark-haired mother stared at him solemnly, from the tinted oval wedding picture hanging over the sofa. She was only seventeen then, his father's second wife. Her sister, his Aunt Barbara, was his father's first wife. She had died from T.B. a few months after they were married — they called it galloping T.B. in those days. His father had married his mother, Vera. Yes, his mother had cried a great deal. Whenever he'd asked her to tell him what was wrong, she'd always reply that she was being foolish. And then she'd go on with her work — never complaining, poor thing, but always crying.

When his father lay dying he'd called out to him. When he had bent down to hear his father, he'd whispered to him — that he'd always loved his mother, had always been faithful to her. He'd wanted John to know that, wanted John to tell his mother that. His father had said that he loved his mother. How could this be, it puzzled him. What a strange thing love was.

It was on the eve of his fourteenth birthday, when it had dawned on him that he had been born only shortly after his parent's marriage. Six months was how he had worked it out — he'd heard his parents quarrelling one night. He'd sat up in his cot in the kitchen listening to their quarrel and he remembered his father shouting words like "whore" and "bitch-in-heat" to his mother. He'd heard his mother's tearful protests, her denials. Her crying broke his heart, and he brooded about what he'd heard. But instead of becoming angry with his father, he would become angry at his mother, disappointed with her. It was sometime after that incident that he'd called his mother "dumb" and got the back of his father's hand across his face. His father had told his mother that "her son" was nothing but a "smart-alec snot-nose". He'd wanted to run to his mother, to ask for her forgiveness but when he saw her stricken face, he couldn't, he was frozen inside.

His father had said he'd loved his mother. Could one trust words? Everything confused him. Whenever he had displeased his father — and it seemed that he'd always displeased him — his father would say, his voice quiet, icy and filled with scorn, that he, John, was "just like his mother". He came to feel that being like his mother, or resembling her family in any way, was a sin. It was a sin for which he was somehow guilty. He used to pray, asking God to make him good, to make him acceptable to his father. He knew he could never hope to please his father, but if only he could avoid displeasing him. Now, his parents were buried side by side. His father would turn over in his grave if he knew that his wife's family was buried alongside him. The last time he'd visited their graves he had noted with sadness that their pictures had faded so much they were not even recognizable. Anyone could have been buried there. Did it matter?

He'd had Elizabeth's body brought home from the funeral parlour, and it had lain here, in this very room. Her mother had protested, had said that it was not done anymore. Their house was too small — where would all the guests find room? But he had insisted. He couldn't bear to leave her in the funeral parlour. It was unthinkable that he would leave her in that hideous room, hushed to make a spectacle for the sympathetic, and the curious. Her closed coffin was banked with flowers and the coffin itself was covered with a large cross of flowers that his mother-in-law had had made up, especially in Edmonton. People had said that never before had they been to a funeral with such beautiful flowers.

The lilacs were at their most beautiful that week, and their scent filled the house and the yard.

People had come to the funeral by car and by buggy, and a group of Elizabeth's former high school friends even hired a Greyhound bus. Anyone passing by the farm could have mistaken the seemingly festive crowd for a wedding party. The day of the funeral was beautiful. There wasn't a cloud in the sky, and the air was cool and dry. One old woman had said to him that it was "lucky" there was no rain, and he had agreed that it was indeed a lovely day. People comforted him, said that it was God's will Elizabeth was taken away. Elizabeth's mother would break out into violent weeping with each well-meaning comment while he'd stared ahead. His heart had turned to ash. Throughout the service, the old priest, who had also married them, delivered the funeral sermon. He talked at great length about the youth, beauty and talent of the dearly departed and of the young and beautiful wife and daughter who would no longer walk among the living. Babich had to support his keening mother-in-law. He had wanted to scream at the priest to stop — to show them some mercy.

When the last of the mourners had left, Babich sat in this same room on the sofa — flanked by his weeping mother-in-law and by Peter's wife Sophie, who did her best to comfort them. In the kitchen, his mother and several old women were washing up the last of the dishes from the dinner that had been served to the mourners.

She would never understand her child's death. Never, never until the day she died. Her only child, just twenty-four years old. She had only started to live. What had *she* done — an old woman who had never hurt anyone in her life — done to deserve this, to be punished in this way? God knows she had never harmed a soul and her voice rose in a wailing sing-song while Sophie Chorney poured her more whiskey. What did young people know of life, she'd asked. What did they understand? Times were so hard when she was young, not like today. Today, everyone wanted to take it easy. What did the young people, today, know of misery? God forgive her, she had confided as she wiped her reddened nose, but she, herself, had had two abortions after Elizabeth was born. She and her husband had no money in those days, and she was nearly forty. She'd had enough misery herself to last a lifetime, coming as she did, from a family of eleven children. Dear God, it had killed her poor mother at thirty-seven. What do young people today know of misery, she'd asked.

When her father brought them to Canada it was November, and they lived in a sod hut, and her mother was pregnant and sick, with only a few potatoes to eat. Her mother dead when, she, the oldest, was only fifteen. Dead God, what is the answer? She had broken into a paroxysm of weeping. Babich had stared ahead, out of this very same window, stared dry-eyed with his heart buried in the heavy oak coffin.

She had understood her daughter and John wanting a good house. She hadn't expected her daughter to live in this chicken-coop. God knows, she could have helped them, if only she had known. I used to say to Elizabeth, when she was growing up, to think hard before she had children. It isn't easy to bring up children, I used to tell her. When you were last over, I told her to put off having children until you get a few pennies together. Did she listen to her mother, to her foolish old mother? God help me if she did.

How my dear husband loved our child. He would have given her his life. When she was born, the doctor told us she wouldn't live. She was so small she fitted into her father's palm. We took turns walking the floor with her night after night, and with God willing we saved our baby. Such a bright child. Always laughing, never a cross word for anyone. Everyone loved her — our house was always full of children — always "Elizabeth this, Elizabeth that" — everyone wanting her attention.

"God, am I to blame? Help me, dear God, help me. God, strike me dead, as I sit here, if I'm to blame."

"What did I know? I am a foolish woman. What did I know? Was I preaching to my child? Did I realize what I was saying? Did I realize that my Elizabeth took my harping as the Gospel? I could never know it would come to this. My child, my child, is dead, and I'll never see her again.

John Babich had no words in him with which to comfort the weeping woman. Her keening was tearing at his heart. He was the guilty one. He was to blame. It was his fault. His fault that Elizabeth was dead.

He remembered that terrible night as if it were yesterday. He would always remember it — seared into his brain.

That night they had gone to bed early, Elizabeth tiring more easily now and feeling quite wretched. She was unable to keep any food down. The morning before she went to school had been particularly difficult for her. Apart from her morning sickness, everything had seemed normal to him. He had teased her about her diet of soda crackers and peppermint candy. She had smiled, saying those were the only things she could keep down.

He had fallen asleep finally after tossing and turning endlessly. How could they manage to build a new house without Elizabeth's salary? He had already spoken to Joseph Litwin about their plans for the new house. He had told his mother-in-law of his plans. The house would be clad in stucco, like her house, but it would be a larger house to accommodate a future family. All Elizabeth had asked for was a porch out front so as not to come directly into the house in wintertime.

Elizabeth's sudden cry of pain had awakened him from a bad dream. She turned to face him, had smiled apologetically. She had said that it was nothing — really, nothing. All she had felt was a tearing pain in her back. Only that. She was fine — really, fine, she was sorry to have startled him so. Then it was gone, the pain was gone and she was really all right.

He had gone over this scene so many times. He had remembered every single thing — everything. He had fallen asleep only after he heard Elizabeth's even and peaceful breathing. He had pulled the bedcovers over her shoulders after she had fallen asleep.

What had happened next was too horrible to even think about. He remembered waking up with a start, feeling that he had wet himself. Startled, he sat up in bed. He could smell it — blood —there was blood on his hands. Sticky blood. He jumped out of bed. "Elizabeth! Elizabeth!" As if in a trance, he stepped into his pants and shoes. He scooped a deathly white Elizabeth out of bed. She was limp and childlike in his arms — like a sleeping child.

The drive to the hospital had been a terrifying nightmare. God, Oh God! Elizabeth, barely able to respond to him, whimpered like a child. Her small face waxen and her hands icy.

He had gone back to sleep when she had been awakened by that pain. Why? Why had he been so willing — no, so anxious — to be assured that she was all right? He should have known her better than that — she never complained. He cursed himself a million times — while his wife lay beside him dying — both of them soaked in her blood. God, Oh God. Could he have saved her? Was he the guilty one? Had he killed her? He would curse himself to his dying day. He, Babich, had killed his beloved Elizabeth. A man such as he did not deserve to live. A man such as Babich is no better than a murderer.

Later, he had watched the mourners as they filed past the casket. His heart a stone as the old people bent to kiss the waxen-like figure in folds of satin. If he didn't get a hold of himself he would lose his mind. The funeral director had taken him to Elizabeth's casket. When he first saw her he had wanted to laugh — he'd had to stifle an impulse to laugh. Laugh? Surely he'd been mad. That strange girl lying there with that odd, pulled smile on her face was not Elizabeth. She was not his wife. He had wanted to run to school, to find Elizabeth, have her reassure him that she was all right. God please help me, he thought, she's in school marking papers. He felt betrayed. Where was she? Where was his beautiful Elizabth? His dear, funny girl. His best friend.

They had dressed her in her best dress — the same pale pink dress she'd worn the night he'd met her, at the teacher's dance. A dress the colour of faded wild rose petals. The collar of her dress had been turned slightly under. And he'd wanted to straighten it out. But the mourners were filing past. And when he looked toward the coffin two strange young men, both so smartly dressed, had stepped up and flanked the coffin. He remembered wondering who they were. He hadn't recognized them. Then, quickly and with a practised and efficient motion, they had tucked the quilted satin in around her, removed the crucifix from the lid of the coffin and had placed it in his hand — all in a single motion, like the wave of a hand. He'd wanted to shout to them, to stop. Had wanted to warm those pale, clenched hands.

Elizabeth was buried in the new cemetery just on the other side of town. His parents had come to stay with him after the funeral. They stayed less than two weeks. His mother had remained in the kitchen all the time and cooked. But he couldn't eat. So she had

Elizabeth's Coffin

wept and scolded him. His father had busied himself around the farm, noting the changes made since he had moved to Edmonton four years before. He had not been pleased with them. Every day had become an endurance test for each of them. And he'd been relieved when he saw them off at the railway station. He wanted to be alone with his memories, alone with Elizabeth again.

He was hanging up his good suit when he'd returned from the station. His parents off, he realized that he was alone — completely alone. For the first time since he'd been a small boy. He had to stifle a feeling of panic — and had gone into the closet to hang up his good suit, when Elizabeth's blue spring coat slipped off the hanger. She had worn that coat often; she had laughingly called it her second skin. He picked the coat up and for a moment held it to him. There was a lingering smell of her perfume on the collar. And he started weeping. It was hopeless. He began to weep uncontrollably. And as he sobbed he'd asked himself over and over again, why had she listened to him, why had she heeded his advice? No one had ever listened to him before. He hadn't known that she would die. His body, racked with sobs, he begged her to come back to him, saying that without her, there was nothing left. He couldn't remember falling asleep, and when he awakened he felt stiff, seared with grief. He'd stumbled out of the house to do his chores — he'd been betrayed. He would never trust anyone ever again. He would never love anyone again. He would let no one come near him. No one would hurt him, ever, again.

It was cold sitting in here, in this room and its smell of mouldy earth. Life had gone by, so quickly, like a quick walk through a dark forest. And here and there, a few rays of sunlight had managed to pierce the darkness. Those short years with Elizabeth had seemed like a stroll over a small sunlit bridge. And then from that sunlit bridge he had passed into this long darkness. With some memories he had left, he had been able to look back from time to time toward that bridge, to warm himself.

The cut on the back of his head still throbbed. When he touched it, he was startled to see blood on his fingers. A stubborn head. It refused to heal. And there he was, again, sitting like an old stump. When there was so much work to do. He had never felt so weary. Babich rose from his chair, left the room, and shut the door quickly. He moved the washstand back in place. The kitchen was nice and warm. He left the house reluctantly. A mournful whistle from the eaves reminded him of the need to finish the work in the garden. Any day soon he would wake up to find frost on the ground.

How beautiful each tomato was. The first basket filled up quickly. And when he had finished, he straightened his back, rested a bit. He couldn't recall a season ever being this bountiful. If only it could stay like this, forever. So he could simply feast his eyes on it for an eternity. The cauliflowers were big, firm, and as white as snow. And the cabbages — they were solid, rock hard and heavy. The weather, praise be to God, was ideal. When he'd finished the first row, he straightened again, surprised to find himself feeling dizzy. He bent his head down. He was getting that dizzy spell again. The temptation to return to the house was strong. But he hated to give in, and so he started on the second row, trying to slow his pace. Each tomato plant was heavy with fruit and there seemed to be no end to them. He was out of breath and his hands felt numb. Straightening up once more, he flexed his fingers and moved his arms to restore the circulation.

Two crows, unusually big and black, circled the pasture and landed on the fence near the barn. Babich stopped to listen to their cawing, watching them as they see-sawed in the wind. Why was it that in spring their cawing seemed so joyful? And now, their cawing only increased his dark feeling of melancholy. It was not yet noon by the sun, but his stomach rumbled with hunger.

Babich moved carefully along the rows of the cauliflowers. He had some cold, boiled potatoes he would fry up quickly. It would be nice to have some fresh boiled cauliflower. He could almost taste it, yet he couldn't bring himself to pick one of the perfect white heads. They were *so* perfect — so flawless. It seemed a shame to cut them down. He'd save them for later, for another day. He continued walking along the row until he found the cauliflower he was looking for. There it was, growing at the very end of the row of perfect cauliflowers, almost hidden by its leaves. A small yellow runt of a cauliflower. It seemed a shame to waste it. He could just as soon eat it, as throw it away, and it would taste almost as good. Babich removed a couple of small tomatoes from a vine, tucked a tomato into each of the pockets of his sweater, and carrying the cauliflower, he returned to the house to cook his noonday meal.

Soon the potatoes were frying in the cast-iron pan, and the little cauliflower was boiling. As Babich waited for his meal to be cooked, he warmed himself and rested. A large fly had come to life in the warm kitchen. He watched it as it buzzed and flew around the window. The fly swatter was handy, at the edge of the washstand, but somehow he hadn't the heart to swat it. Somehow, its lively buzzing cheered him. He continued to watch it as he ate his simple meal, while standing at the stove. He couldn't remember when he'd enjoyed a meal as much as this. When he'd finished, he topped off his meal with several dippers of fresh cold water. Now, he felt pretty good. The temptation to lie down and to take a little nap was strong, but again he resisted. There was still too much work left. Babich turned up the shawl collar of his sweater and brought it closer to his neck. He repinned the safety pin to hold it in place. When he came out again, the sun had almost disappeared behind a large cloud. Cloud shadows moved across the fields and pasture. He started back on the second row of tomatoes and continued working steadily, his breathing now coming in short, shallow gasps. The damned pain was plaguing him again. But he wouldn't let it get to him, and he continued bending down, slowly, down the second row, and even more slowly, he began on the third row. The baskets of tomatoes shone brightly, like jewels in the sun, and the sight of them gave him the impetus to continue. In a little while the sun came out again, but the wind continued to blow, and caused his eyes to tear. Exasperated with himself, he stopped to wipe away his tears with the sleeve of his sweater. And just when he looked up, a gust of wind divided the weeds and grasses in the pasture, exposing a single bright flower. Again, tears welled up and he wiped them away again, angry for his foolishness. Crying, like a sentimental young girl over a flower. After awhile the setting sun disappeared behind the barn. The garden was veiled by the long shadow of the barn.

Soon all the available baskets were filled. There was nothing to do, but go to the shed for more baskets. There was an entire row of tomatoes left untouched and it seemed to him that each plant was more heavily laden than its neighbour. Was nature mocking his age and infirmity? He'd get up, earlier, tomorrow. The baskets were heavier than he'd expected; he half-carried, half-dragged them into the house, and arranged the baskets in a row in the cool pantry. If Mrs. Ellefson kept her word, she'd be in tomorrow and maybe buy other vegetables as well. He was breathing heavily when he'd dragged the last basket into the house. It was nearly dark when he came out of the house again. He surveyed his garden, pleased with the day's work. He'd done a pretty good job — a pretty good job for an old man.

Suddenly, a loud noise, sharp as a rifle crack, startled him. The damned doors to the loft were slamming in the wind. He'd just have to go up and wire them shut before they drove him crazy. They'd slammed off and on all last night. The wind had started dying down a bit. It would have been a good day for airing his bedding. Maybe he would do it tomorrow. Babich walked toward the barn slowly,

Baning Barn Door

stopping every few feet to rest, and to catch his breath.

Bats darted in and out of the open loft. He stopped to watch them as they wheeled and circled over the pasture, diving and swooping in their search for food. He was almost at the barn when he remembered. The dream. That terrifying dream last night. He certainly wasn't a superstitious old woman who believed in dreams. Yet the memory of last night's dream came back to him vividly. He couldn't bring himself to enter the dark and empty barn. Let those doors slam away. He would see better what he was doing in broad daylight anyway. Probably couldn't find a suitable piece of wire, just because he needed it. He was too tired to climb up anyway. Babich turned to walk back to the house when he noticed the rakes leaning against the barn. He had wasted the morning searching for them yesterday. He picked them up and entered the old barn which had been used as a tool shed for many years. The shed was clean and orderly; he'd done a good job cleaning up last week. His father would have been pleased. It had taken nearly three days to get it in order. Babich looked around for a rag, wiped the rakes off carefully, then added them to the neat rows of garden tools that lined the mud-plastered walls. The room could use a good coat of whitewash. Next spring he'd have to find the time, as well as fill in the chinks where the mudplaster had dropped off. There was always plenty of work on the farm. Something scurried over Babich's foot and startled him. Something small and dark. He caught a glimpse of it as it darted under one of the stalls. It was only a little field mouse but the little creature had scared him.

Babich looked around for a place to sit, and settled on an upturned oil drum. It felt cold under him so he peeled off a faded chenille bedspread that he used to protect his new aluminum stepladder, folded it under himself, and sat down again. There were still many things he could clear out. The shelves on the wall sagged with the weight of tins and jars. Things collected throughout the years, boxes full of horseshoes, piles of Eaton's and Simpson's catalogues, useless things. Somehow, he couldn't bear to throw some things away. Two of the stalls were filled to the top with firewood, and it comforted him to see the neatly stacked piles. With him using just the two rooms, there was plenty of wood for two winters. Babich loaded several pieces of wood onto his arm when there was another loud bang outside. He dropped the wood and peered out. Forgetting to stoop down, he struck his forehead, hard, on the door frame. Cursing, he decided he'd better wire that door up — wire it once and for all. There was a large roll of clothesline wire he'd left some time stored back in a box in the garage. Babich closed the door to the shed and looked up at the evening sky. He rubbed his forehead. It was going to be a truly beautiful night!

Next week definitely, he'd go into town, get some coffee and that oilcloth. He had been thinking about his will too, and God knows he should change it. Left everything to the church in town. A nice little sum of money too. What they did with it didn't really matter to him — he'd be six feet under. Still, it seemed a shame to spend his hard-earned money on yet another fancy chandelier. If they weren't careful, one of these days the church roof would come down on them from the weight of those chandeliers. Maybe it was blasphemous to even think it. But that new priest was quite hopeless. He couldn't hear him, let alone understand him —speaking like that, in that whine — like he'd been constipated for days. How did he expect to keep us awake with that sing-song of his? Why couldn't he speak out with joy so an old man could go home with something? Yes, he'd talk it over with that lawyer; he could advise him. Maybe better to leave the money to the old folks home. Who knows what the future might bring. Might end up there one of these days myself.

There was a faint smell of burning leaves in the air. A full moon was rising, and for one fleeting aching moment, he felt fifteen again.

The garage was at the opposite end of the yard. Before he reached it he had to stop several times to rest, to catch his breath. Babich lifted the latch to the door. As he opened the heavy door, the top hinge pulled away from the rotted wood and the door sagged. Groaning with effort, Babich lifted and dragged the clumsy door, opening it just enough to permit him to enter the garage. There was a faint smell of gas, oil and damp earth in the garage. A pleasant smell that never failed to remind him of his childhood.

It had been many years since he had driven a car. He'd been driving home from town one day when it suddenly occurred to him. He could easily hit one of the children walking along the road —one moment of his inattention, and he could injure, or even kill an innocent child — could he live with a terrible thing like that on his conscience, he'd asked himself. He told himself that he was too old to drive anyway. So he drove the old De Soto into the garage and left it there. Birds and pigeons had gotten into the garage and used his De Soto for roosting. Its black roof and sides were now white with their droppings. Babich hesitated for just a moment, opened the door to the driver's seat, and got in. The marble-patterned steering wheel felt icy cold.

The long walk through the dew-covered grass had soaked his pantlegs. He felt tired. His stomach was complaining, but he continued to sit in his car, in the quiet of the garage. Outside the garage, birds chirped in sleep. The branches of the lilac trees around the garage bent in the wind, making scratching sounds on the roof. But Babich scarcely heard. A collection of old licence plates, all arranged in neat rows, relieved the gloom of the dark and stained walls of the garage. Some of the licence plates came from their Model A Ford — what a sweet little car that had been. That time they'd taken his calf to Bellis — squeezed the suffering animal into the back seat of their little Ford. He couldn't say that was one of his happier memories, but thinking about it later, it had seemed very funny.

His father had sometimes done some strange things, some very odd things, indeed. Always did things his way. Nothing his mother, or grandmother ever said could change him. Once his mind was made up, that was it! What a miserable trip that had been, ploughing through those gumbo roads. His mother, as instructed by his father, had covered the back seat with a horse blanket and some gunny sacks, and he, as instructed, had joined the calf in the back seat. The calf was unhappy from the moment she got shoved into the car. It had bawled all the way into town. Every time she had squirmed, she had squashed him against the seat. All through the trip, he'd been sorely tempted to beg his father to turn back, but instead held on to the heavy calf for dear life. And, suffered in silence. Over and over the poor calf would try to climb into the driver's seat, or over the side of the open car. Every time they had slowed down at the crossroads, or at the railway crossing the calf would make another bid for freedom. Every time they had passed a herd of cows, the calf would start bawling, and some wild-eyed cow would come running to investigate. His father had screamed instructions to him all the way to Bellis, prefacing each sentence with "dumb-bell" and "idiot". So that when they had finally arrived at the stockyard, he had felt more relieved than sorry, as the calf leaped into the filthy pen of the stockyard, awash with pools of yellow rainwater, floating with manure.

He remembered getting a bag of jelly-beans. His mother had got the Fleischmann's yeast that she had requested, and Mr. Sawchuck got his bill paid for the bindertwine his father had bought on credit some months before. To make amends with him, his father had told him, as a kind of joke between them, that it was lucky that the calf didn't drop any cow-pies on his lap. Come to think of it, he had been lucky.

The summer he had turned fourteen, that was a summer to remember. That was the year his cousin Victoria married her handsome R.C.M.P. officer. What excitement there'd been over the wedding. His grandmother and mother talked of nothing but the wedding for weeks. His father and the two women had left for the wedding in Smoky Lake at the crack of dawn. He had stayed home to do the chores. Actually, he had looked forward to having the day entirely to himself. Minutes after the green Ford had disappeared around the bend in the road, he was circling the barn in their new John Deere tractor — it was heaven. But he was just putting in time until the afternoon when Peter would arrive. Then the day would really begin. He'd made a big pitcher of Rawleigh's orange drink for himself. He had gone in and out of the house eating the doughnuts his grandmother had fried especially for him. He had let the screen door slam shut behind him every time he entered or left the house. There was no one to scold him that day.

He felt like a king. He floated through the morning, finished all his chores, and filled the trough to overflowing. The water seemed to gush out of the pump without any effort on his part. He felt frisky as a colt. Fireflies whirled over the yard, their wings jewel-bright in the sun. He had watched them dreamily as they skimmed over the rotted manure pile behind the barn. Waiting for him and Peter were two packages of Sweet Caps hidden in his dresser, waiting to be smoked. This was the day he and Peter Chorney had been waiting for. As they walked home from school they had laid their plans carefully. He was to wait for the signal from Peter. It wasn't going to be too easy for Peter to get away. Peter always had a lot of chores on Saturday. He'd solemnly promised Peter that he wouldn't start on the cigarettes until Peter arrived. He'd crossed his heart and hoped to die he wouldn't. He'd squatted in the cool shade behind the barn, where he could just barely make out where the two Chorneys were working, two tiny figures bobbing in the distance. Poor Peter, he and his father were, as usual, breaking their backs picking stones. Clearing their land of stones. He'd helped Peter many times. It seemed to him that Peter's father was forever dragging out that miserable stoneboat, and forever dragging his friend Peter with him.

By late afternoon, Peter and he were down to the last two cigarettes of the first package. One more pack of Sweet Caps to go. Although he remembered feeling a little sick, it had been so pleasant sitting there. They were both practising blowing smoke rings when suddenly their idyll was over. Even their old Holstein, Bossie, and their companion for the afternoon, had got to her feet when she'd heard the loud shouting. Where had Mr. Chorney come from? They never did figure it out. And though they had laughed about it years later, that afternoon they didn't laugh much. For a fat man, Peter's father had moved with amazing speed and agility. Red-faced and sputtering with rage, Mr. Chorney had confronted them with the evidence! Each one of them with a cigarette in his hand, and the trampled grass in front of them bearing evidence of their heavy smoking. He'd called them both "good-for-nothing bums". With a well-placed kick that had sent Peter flying, he had ruined their sunny afternoon. He watched as Peter and his father disappeared over the hill. Just the rise and fall of the willow switch indicating their progress. He'd gone to bed that night with Mr. Chorney's warning ringing in his ears. His father would be notified as soon as he saw him. And he, John, would get a good licking too.   All night he had tossed and turned. It was dawn when he heard voices in the kitchen — raised, angry voices. There was something odd about the noises. It was unheard of, but for the first and only time ever, he'd heard his mother's voice raised, not shouting, but loud enough for his father to keep asking her to shut up. To stop yelling, lest she wake their sleeping son. He never got a scolding for the smoking incident. It was never even mentioned! He had never known whether Mr. Chorney had ever betrayed him. But always, in his mind he'd credited the little green Ford with saving his hide.

His mother and grandmother had served breakfast that morning. They took turns telling him about the wedding. It had been a beautiful wedding — so many people, maybe three-hundred people — Victoria had looked like an angel, with her eight bridesmaids, each wearing dresses like the colours of the rainbow. And the gifts, gifts like for royalty, gifts that overflowed the hall stage. The groom looked so handsome in his R.C.M.P. uniform. All the girls, and the women too, had sighed over him. Yes, of course, it *was* true, unfortunately he was an Englishman, but still, in spite of it, he seemed such a nice, humble young man. After all, Victoria had to wait all those years, until he got his permission to marry. If Victoria loved him that much, such a nice girl, it said something for the young man. As for the rest, his mother had indicated with a jerk of her head, that he should ask his father. His father had something to tell him. His father had remained silent throughout breakfast, his face lowered into his dish of porridge.

Later, as they had crossed the field that morning, his father tried to explain how the terrible accident had come to pass. His father had said that it didn't make sense, this accident that had happened. No one would believe him, his father had said, because to tell the truth, he still couldn't believe it himself. God knows, if he weren't being punished for some sins he didn't even know about! He worked alongside his unusually subdued father. And then when he saw, with his own eyes, what had happened, he'd had to agree with his father that their little green Ford was "caput". It certainly was "caput".

What else could any one call it — that twisted burnt-out shell. That charred skeleton — there — before their eyes! There really were no two ways about it, the little green Ford was finished. He'd been very tired, his father had explained to him somewhat lamely. John had stared ahead, not wishing to meet his father's eyes. His father was suffering. The smell of whiskey on his father's breath had been so strong he'd had to step back. To save time, his father had explained he'd decided to cut through the Ruptash farm, thinking it would be a short-cut, and just like that, this is what happened. His father had snapped his fingers to indicate to him just how quickly the whole catastrophe had happened. The scene before him was amazing. It was funny, and sad and somehow beautiful, all at the same time. He'd stared in silence at the burnt-out hulk and at the blackened perimeter of what had been the Ruptash strawpile. Bits of white ash and straw floated lazily in the air. The stench of rubber lingered in the area for days after. The women had yelled, his father said, thinking he was about to hit a cow. They had so confused him with their yelling that, just to satisfy them he'd turned the wheel of the car sharply. This is what happened!

They had hurried back home to avoid meeting the seven Ruptash children who'd come running to view the wreck, all shouting gleefully over the unexpected bonanza. That morning as they had hurried home he told his father about the Vikings that he'd been studying about in school. And to comfort his father, he told him that because the accident had happened this way, his father had given their car a Viking funeral. His father had liked that. For years he'd listen to his father relate to them about the time he'd given his Ford a proper Viking funeral. Everyone who listened would laugh heartily. But his father's laugh was always the heartiest.

Babich was chilled, cold as a corpse, sitting here in this dark car. Yet he couldn't seem to get a move on. Through the partly-open garage door he could see the moon rising. A big beautiful harvest moon. It would be a lovely night. A night for young people to dream on.

Babich was content. He had never wanted much. And as he grew older, he needed even less. To tell the truth, he knew more about life and the world around him when he was young, more than he knew now. Once he could feel beauty around him. Now he was like a lame old horse wearing blinkers. His farm had become his whole life. His world. He'd never been anywhere. The furthest he'd been from home had been to Edmonton. And he'd always been glad to get back home to the farm. All those people in Edmonton scurrying around. Rushing, God knows where. Rushing to their death. All of us, all alike. A sense of peace came over him. He'd been a lucky man. Never had he dreamed that Elizabeth would ever become his wife. He hadn't even dreamed that she would look at him, a nobody. A poor simple farmer.

Their marriage, their few years together still seemed a miracle to him. She had loved him. He'd had his miracle. He couldn't ask for more. Old people who remembered, still talked of her gaiety, of her beauty, her kindness. If you'd met John's wife they'd say, you'd have seen a real beauty, and the young people only half-listening, would feign interest. He knew very well what they were thinking. This miserable old man, this bag of bones, this old scarecrow standing before them. Impossible! He'd heard the youngsters make fun of him; he wasn't deaf, and his tears started again. She had never left his heart. Or his mind. He had never wanted another woman. He'd told Peter that once. He'd been hurt and puzzled when Peter had snorted. It didn't matter what anyone thought —nothing mattered anymore. He was content.

His Elizabeth had had a quick temper but they had never stayed angry with one another. Never! Even that time when they had visited Elizabeth's mother in Willingdon. His mother-in-law had written them a letter saying she'd finished making their anniversary gift. They'd been married nearly a year and she suggested that they drive over for dinner, and pick up their present at the same time. On the way home from Willington a heavy rain had started, and their car had slid into a water-filled ditch. He'd tried to get the car out. But in the end, a farmer living nearby had to come to their rescue. He hoisted their car out with his team of horses. For some reason he and Elizabeth had started arguing and then quarreling over nothing. She'd called him a "stupid farmer", and he'd driven home hurt and angry. It had been dusk when they had arrived home. Elizabeth had run ahead of him to the house while he had put the car in the garage. Then he carried the parcels — some preserves and a beautiful cross-stitched bedspread that had been his mother-in-law's gift to them. He remembered that it had stopped raining and he had stopped to admire the rainbow that stretched from their pasture over to the Chorney house. Elizabeth had been waiting at the front door. She'd forgotten that he had the key to the house, and she'd become very angry because he had taken so much time getting to the house. He remembered her looking like a drowned kitten. He'd only wanted to tease her a little, had longed to take her into his arms. But she'd avoided looking at him. When he'd opened the door she'd just brushed right past him into the house. He'd walked in and placed the things on the kitchen table. He had taken a good look around their sparsely furnished house, and wondered what he'd been thinking. She was right. He was stupid; he *was* just a stupid farmer. The contrast between their little house and her mother's large house in Willingdon — it was painful to even compare them. He was determined then, as that moment, that if he never did anything else, he would build Elizabeth the biggest and the most beautiful house in the district. He'd show that mother of her's: so smug and self-satisfied. He'd show his father! He'd show everyone! He'd show his father that he was a "hospodar".

After all these years, that evening long ago remained clear in his mind. Even now, whenever he heard a meadowlark, memories of that evening came back. On summer evenings when he smelled the scent of the tobacco plant, a sweet sorrow filled his heart. And he'd always think of that night, always of Elizabeth. In his dreams he'd be waiting for her, always filled with longing but also filled with such despair. He knew that day by day, he was growing older: a knowing certainty, that it would always be too late for him. Sometimes in a dream a stranger would come to their house. He'd say that he'd heard Elizabeth had returned. Babich would dress hurriedly, afraid he'd miss her. He'd rush out calling her name. But everything held him back, conspired against him finding her, and he'd give up. And just then she would appear. She always looked the way she did that night — her large dark eyes would study him, gravely. As a small child regards a stranger. And when he'd reached out to take her hand, she'd turn away from him quietly, not saying a word. She would disappear, and he'd call out to her, begging her to listen to him — to come back to him. When he awakened his face would be wet with tears. And a feeling of deep loss, a heavy melancholy, would cling to him all the next day.

The dream and the memories were all he had left of her. So he nourished these memories. He could not permit them to fade. He could forget where he'd put his rakes. Or he'd fill the sugar bowl with salt, or a dozen foolish things an old man sometimes does —things that bedevilled and plagued him — but that memorable night would stay as bright and fresh as though he had just experienced it.

That summer day, so long time ago, Elizabeth had gone into the bedroom and he could hear her moving about. He'd stood in the kitchen, feeling clumsy and bewildered, uncertain. His clothes were soaking wet, and dripped on the linoleum floor. He was chilled to the bone, felt like a fool standing there. For some reason he would never understand, he'd always felt shy of the girl in the bedroom.

Even after they'd been married a year they were still like polite strangers. He couldn't rid himself of the feeling he had — that she'd pack up and leave him. In the evenings when she'd been working on her school register, or correcting piles of students' homework, he'd find himself watching her. He wanted to remember exactly what she looked like. She was so beautiful, so fragile; he was always afraid of hurting her. She'd often teased him, reminding him she wasn't breakable.

Later that evening she'd returned to the kitchen barefooted, wearing only her slip. Her hair was damp and she had tied it back, away from her face with a ribbon. Her cheeks were flushed and her eyes sparkled. She had looked at him, standing there in his wet clothes, and teased him. She had called him her own sweet westwind: he'd felt the warmth rising in him, and then she was in his arms, kissing him with so much passion he felt breathless. He'd been so taken aback by her change of mood that he'd stood motionless. So she had kissed him again and again, and with cool, child-like hands, unbuttoned his wet jacket, his wet shirt. With her face against his chest, they shivered in the warm kitchen.

His heart hammered. He could scarcely breathe. He'd wanted to cry — tears of relief — she had said she loved him the first time she'd met him, that he'd been so handsome and arrogant when she'd first seen him. She told him he would always be her kind, generous, dear love. She hoped he'd forgive her when she'd been mean. Suddenly, anything and everything seemed possible. The world felt beautiful. He remembered that a warm evening breeze had been blowing that night. The smell of tobacco plants growing near the kitchen window had filled the house. Her soft, dark hair brushed against his neck, smelled of rain. She had felt so loving, so gentle in his arms. The next morning when he awakened at dawn, her body, slender, curved against him. He'd been afraid to move, afraid he'd wake her, so he had watched her as light gradually filled their bedroom. He felt tender, brushed the hair off her face, watched her sleep. He loved her and he'd work harder than ever. He'd give her everything. She would be proud of him. That moment he had never felt so happy — so whole. Later that day he'd become afraid of this happiness. Would he be punished for this joy? Did he deserve such happiness? That day he'd walked up to the school, held her hand all the way home — he'd been so afraid of something happening to her, afraid he'd lose her.

Babich stirred. It was crazy to sit here like this freezing to death. In slow motion, he got out from behind the wheel, shut the car door behind him. It bothered him to leave the garage door hanging. He tried lifting the door, surprised to find it so heavy he could scarcely lift it. He put his shoulder against the door, lifting and pushing he was able to close and latch the door. Damned if he was going to let those doors get the best of him. It was relatively warm outside compared to the garage. Babich walked through the grass, back to the house. The moon had risen. He watched as a cloud moved over it. It really was a fine night.

Out of force of habit, Babich glanced toward the Chorney farm. It was dark and quiet. Not a thing moved. The gentle darkness embraced him. He felt weary, but content. He had done what he set out to do. He'd done a good days work — put things in order. The breeze lifted a few dry leaves from the grass, resettled them. At the other end of the yard he heard the barn doors slam again. Damn it! He had forgotten all about the wire. And the slamming doors only reminded him of his stupidity.

The wooden sidewalk from the pump to the house creaked, groaned under his feet. Tired as he was, he could not resist taking another look at his garden. In the moonlight his garden looked especially beautiful. The cabbages and cauliflowers gleamed. He sat down on the stoop to pull off his boots. The silence of the night was broken by the cry of a coyote. Astonished, he hadn't heard a coyote for God knows how long. The sound never failed to fill him with awe. Again, but faintly this time, the cry sounded. Once more the howl, but this time it came from the direction of the slough.

Babich couldn't believe his good luck. Hearing the coyote after having had such a day. It was a perfect way to end a beautiful day.

The moonlit kitchen was pleasant and warm. He could hear

The Coyote Baying

from the warning sizzle that the washbasin at the back of the stove was nearly empty. Babich found a match, touched it to the hot stove, lit the coal-oil lamp and placed it on the table. He had refused to have the house wired for electricity. Maybe he'd been too hasty. He'd have to reconsider it. Maybe next spring he would get those young fellows to come wire the house. He was tired of fighting. So many things needed fixing around the house. He had forgotten to clean the lamp chimney so the light was dim. He just couldn't keep up with all these things anymore. Babich picked up several pieces of wood from the oven, stoked the stove, added water to the basin and put the coffee pot back on the stove.

His sweater was damp, felt as itchy as the devil. Babich pulled it over his head, stepped out of his overalls and hooked both garments onto a nail behind the stove. He poured a cup of coffee and stood by the stove, sipping it. The water in the basin had started to simmer. He put the pan on the washstand, and washed his hands and face. The hot washcloth felt good. He applied it to his face several times, and wiped the damp hair away from his face. His reflection in the mirror above the washstand startled him. Jesus Christ he looked like a mad dog! The hot water had opened his cut lip. He felt the trickle of blood on his chin and neck. He could taste warm blood in his mouth, spat it out into the slop-pail. His face would frighten the dead. Who, now, would call him handsome? A shadow of a smile flickered across his face at the thought. He should be ashamed — his underwear was grey, filthy. It needed a good scrubbing. Babich unbuttoned his longjohns, stepped out of them, and draped them over the warming oven to dry.

Naked, shivering, Babich walked into the cold bedroom. He rummaged through the jammed drawers in his dresser. He found the things he needed and went into the kitchen. He stood by the warm stove, put on his clean underwear, removed a shirt from its cellophane wrapping and put it on. Then he sat down to pull on some clean white socks. He returned to the bedroom and came back carrying his good black suit. It was no use fooling himself. His pain was so intense that he had trouble buttoning his trousers. His hands trembled. The suit jacket hung like a tent on his emaciated frame. He'd buttoned his shirt incorrectly, but it didn't matter. It would do. His good Sunday suit made him feel boyish, strangely festive. He was ten years old again, in the school concert at Smoky Lake. The wood in the stove shifted and fell. It crackled, and the smell of coffee filled the kitchen.

There was a cold wind coming from somewhere. The bedroom window. He'd left it open this morning. Babich returned to the bedroom and tried to close it. It refused to budge. The wind was cold on his face. As he stood there, the pain in his chest was strong. It took his breath away. He grabbed the windowsill for support. He held on as the pain intensified. The moon, large, was bright orange. He focussed on it — to ease the pain. He felt imprisoned now as the orange moon floated, then swam away from him. He was desperate. He took a deep breath. As the moon floated back, the pain seemed to recede.

The bed was as he had left it. Two grey flannel blankets covered the mattress, which was stained. Two pillows were without pillowcases. The ticking was grey, filthy from years of use. His body rigid, Babich pulled off the two blankets, folded them neatly and placed them on the top of the dresser. Carefully and deliberately, he opened the large chest at the foot of his bed. Reverently, he removed a bedspread from the neatly folded piles of embroidered and cross-stitched linens. He shook out the spread and covered his bed with it, smoothing it neatly. The snow-white spread shone, its borders of cross-stitches transformed his dismal room. The pain in his heart was persistent. It forced him to hang on to the edge of the bed. Beads of perspiration formed on his temples and forehead. He felt the perspiration trickling. It was as if a giant hand were crushing him. He couldn't breathe. Dear God in Heaven, help me. Dear God in Heaven. Help me, he repeated. He wanted water — a glass of water. He was suffocating. Hunched over, he tried to get to the kitchen. He couldn't make it, held on to the door frame for support. For a moment the giant hand eased its grip. He moved slowly back to his bed. He eased himself onto the clean white bed. The pain came again, was rising now. A tidal wave lifted him, then dropped him. He was being sucked under, in an undertow. He tried to cross himself, but the pain in his arm and chest was too intense. His arm fell across his chest. He brought his other hand over it. He clasped his hands together in an attitude of prayer.

He tried to pray, but his brain wouldn't respond. He was slipping off the smooth rock shelf where he stood. He was being swept under again. Going down, down into a dark, bottomless valley. He held on, desperately. He wasn't ready yet. The sound of his voice echoed through the house. "God forgive me, Oh God forgive me." The pain subsided, left him! A gentle voice spoke to him — assured him that pain wouldn't bother him again. Babich lifted his head, looked around. There was no one in the room. No one beside him. But he felt calm, and peaceful.

The bedroom was beautiful in the moonlight. He felt the tension in his body leaving. He felt free, and light. A light breeze blew in through the open window, Babich could smell freshly mown hay. He breathed deeply. The same gentle voice was warning him now that the pain would soon return. But it didn't matter to him anymore. Nothing could hurt him. Nobody could hurt him. He closed his eyes. He saw himself walking down a long corridor filled with light. He felt confident. As light as air. There, at the end of the corridor, just as he had expected, was a light beckoning — to him. He walked eagerly toward it. He wanted to feel its warmth. As he drew nearer he was filled with an absolute yearning — to touch the light. A longing to embrace it. Babich reached out to touch it. A voice was calling out a name. His name. John Onufrey Babich. The voice was clear. There was no mistake. John Onufrey Babich. He felt safe. Protected. You're next, John, the voice said. He wasn't afraid. He knew the words, knew them by heart. He could see his father and mother, there in the front row. His father was looking down at the floor. He could see his mother looking up towards the stage. Love shining in her eyes. That gentle voice called out his name, again: John Onufrey Babich. He walked out, confidently. The way Mrs. Rudyk had instructed him to do. His palms were wet. He looked straight at the audience. He knew all the words perfectly. His voice was clear as a bell. His voice carried throughout the hall. Tonight, he knew, his father would be proud, of him, his father would love him.

DEATH OF THE CHICKEN MAN

by Rostyslav Bratun.

Coyotes howl.
Farmer Ivan Babych is dying.
Widower Ivan Babych is dying.
Ivan Babych, nicknamed Chicken Man is dying.
His large bed exhales icy breath —
having long forgotten the passion of youth.
Ivan Babych pulls his green coverlet over himself; it is his field —
Still green, as when he had once proclaimed;
"field, you are *mine*."
He pulls the field toward himself — over himself.
He wants to cover himself with his field.
He wants to enshroud his dying self
in this green bounty — in this winter crop chill —
. . . and white angels come to Ivan Babych —
White angels — his chickens.
They surround his green bed,
mourning their master
departing this sinful world.

> Chickens turn into angels
> when their master dies.
> He, who gave them seed and water, —
> He, who will never again stand
> on the threshold to call to them.
> (. . .)
> Now they are helpless
>   like their chicken god. Chicken man
>   Ivan Babych

. . . and the angel-chickens cluck reverentially —
surround the green field of their master's bed;
their chicken god, Chicken man. Ivan Babych.
  The Blessed Virgin looks down upon him
  from an ikon, given by his mother, —
      smiles sorrowfully —
  since it was she who blessed him
  when he started out on his journey
  in order to turn from Ivan Babych
  into the Chicken man.

        Dogs bay

He nestles his head into his pillow
as though into his mother's palms.

He pulls his green field toward himself — over himself —
in order to hide under it.

. . . and the Black Rooster appears —
    Black Rooster — Death

The Black Rooster crows — summons Ivan Babych,
the Chicken man, into the chicken paradise
where he will never worry about his daily bread —
neither for himself — nor for his angel — chickens.
  Ivan Babych escapes the crowing
  of the Black Rooster —
hides under the green field — his green coverlet —
his strength is ebbing — he cannot flee.

. . . and his unsold tomatoes, filling baskets —
    mock him for his unfulfilled life.

Ivan Babych wants to confess,
but his angel — chickens do not listen.
The Black Rooster crows frenziedly.
Coyotes howl in the starkly silent prairie.

Departing from the chicken world,
Ivan Babych hears these bitter words;
"The harvest is passed,
the summer is ended,
and we are not saved."

Doors slam in the empty hay-loft,
where once lay the coffin of his wife.

Coyotes howl.
Black Rooster crows.

Ivan Babych strains mightily
to slip beneath his green coverlet.
The angel-chickens sing;
"Amen!"

While on a visit to Canada, well-known Ukrainian poet, Rostyslav Bratun, saw William Kurelek's illustrations for The Chicken Man on exhibit at the Winnipeg Art Gallery.

The cover illustration inspired The Death of the Chicken Man. This poem is from a collection of his poems entitled My Father's Testament (Kiev, 1981). It was translated from Ukrainian by Lydia Palij.